Introduction

VIZ Media has an excellent lineup of awesome new manga for 2015. From lighthearted romantic comedies to dark dramas, this year has one of the most exciting range of titles that we've published yet. We hope you enjoy this sampler of some of our favorite new series.

Table of Contents

Twin Star Exorcists: Onmyoji

Story and Art by Yoshiaki Sukeno

Rokuro dreams of becoming anything but an exorcist! Then mysterious Benio turns up. The pair are dubbed the "Twin Star Exorcists" and learn they are fated to marry... Can Rokuro escape both fates?

SOUSEI NO ONMYOJI © 2013 by Yoshiaki Sukeno /SHUEISHA Inc.

So Cute It Hurts!!

Story and Art by Go Ikeyamada

The Kobayashi twins, Megumu and Mitsuru, were named after historical figures, but only Megumu has grown up with a taste for history. So when Mitsuru is in danger of losing his weekends to extra history classes, he convinces his sister to swap clothes with him and ace his tests! After all, how hard can it be for them to play each other?

...BUT I ALSO LOVE KOJU X MASA CUZ IT'S SO IMMORAL.

I FIND THE DATE X SANA RIVALRY STIRRING...

I HAD LONG CHATS ON TWITTER WITH OTHER YUSUKE FANS!

I HAVE NO IDEA WHAT THEY'RE TALKING ABOUT!

MASTER-SERVANT RELATIONSHIPS GOTTA BE SERVANT X MASTER ROLE REVERSALS...

THEY'RE DIE-HARD OTAKU, ALTHOUGH THEY DON'T LOOK LIKE IT!

...AND THE POLITE TOP X THE ARROGANT BOTTOM...

SO THAT'S WHY THEY GET ALONG WITH MEGO...

I'LL BE A FUJIYAMA FAN AS LONG AS I LIVE.

I'M THINKING ABOUT MAKING A NEW SIGN FOR THEIR NEXT LIVE SHOW. ♡ ♡

His best response.

Y-YEAH.

SERVANT-MASTER AND YUSUKE FANS ARE BOTH GREAT.

Meanwhile...

GLOOM

GOD OF WAR

FIGHT OF WAR

123

BATTLE READY

AKECHI BOYS HIGH SC

BOW BEFORE US

BOO!

Mego, cross-dressed as Mitsuru

BOOM BOOM

SHAK

CHOMP CHOMP

WH... WHAT'S GOING ON HERE...?

I ENDED UP GOING TO MITSURU'S SCHOOL...

MITSURU KOBA-YAAAAH!

I'LL KEEP QUIET...

...SO NO ONE NOTICES—

STOMP STOMP

10 feet tall

...BUT I DIDN'T KNOW THE STUDENTS WERE SO BAD!

SPECIAL
THANKS

Yuka Ito-sama,
Rieko Hirai-sama,
Kayoko Takahashi-sama,
Kawasaki-sama,
Nagisa Sato Sensei.

Rei Nanase Sensei,
Arisu Fujishiro Sensei,
Mumi Mimura Sensei,
Masayo Nagata-sama,
Naochan-sama,
Asuka Sakura Sensei,
and many others.

Bookstore Dan
Kinshicho Branch,
Kinokuniya Shinjuku
Branch, LIBRO Ikebukuro
Branch, Kinokuniya
Hankyu 32-Bangai
Branch.

Sendai Hachimonjiya
Bookstore, Books
HOSHINO Kintetsu
Pass'e Branch, Asahiya
Tennoji MiO Branch,
Kurashiki Kikuya
Bookstore.

Salesperson:
Mizusawa-sama

Previous salesperson:
Honma-sama

Previous editor:
Nakata-sama

Current editor:
Shoji-sama

I also sincerely express
my gratitude to
everyone who
picked up this volume.

SLAM

CRASH

I THINK CLASS A IS OVER THAT WAY—

UUUUH.

WAH?!

AZUSA TOKUGAWA.

I WANNA EXCHANGE EMAIL ADDRESSES WITH HER ♪

SODA

Coke

So upbeat

...

YOU ALL RIGHT?

HERE, DRY OFF WITH THIS.

COME ON, LOOK UP—

THUMP...

YOU'RE
...

A FAINT
AROMA.

THE GENTLE
FRAGRANCE
OF LAVENDER.

IT'S AS IF
THE SCENT IS
USHERING
HER...

...LOVE MIRACLE.

...OF HER FIRST AND MOST MOMENTOUS...

...TO THE BEGINNING...

To be continued in **So Cute It Hurts!!**, Vol. 1

Tokyo Ghoul

Story and Art by Sui Ishida

Ghouls live among us, the same as normal people in every way—
except their craving for human flesh.

Ken Kaneki is an ordinary college student until a violent encounter
turns him into the first half-human half-ghoul hybrid. Trapped
between two worlds, he must survive Ghoul turf wars, learn more
about Ghoul society and master his new powers.

JINGLE JINGLE

...!!!

WHAT IF THEY BAN US FROM--

OOPS, I'M SORRY!

...?

...!!

OVER THERE... THAT'S HER...

WHAT'S WRONG, DUDE?

SHE WAS SO CUTE I COULDN'T HELP MYSELF!

...?

THE BOOK IS ABOUT A COLD-BLOODED FEMALE SERIAL KILLER CALLED THE "BLACK GOAT" AND HER ONLY SON.

ALTHOUGH HER SON IS DISGUSTED WITH HIS MOTHER'S SICKNESS...

...HE EVENTUALLY HAS TO ACKNOWLEDGE THE SAME CRUEL IMPULSES GROWING INSIDE HIM.

AH.

AH.

WHOA, SHE'S COMING THIS WAY.

THE WRITING INTERTWINES INTENSE EXPRESSIONS WITH DELICATE PSYCHOLOGICAL DESCRIPTIONS. IT'S SEN TAKATSUKI'S SEVENTH BOOK...

OH...?

I-I'M SORRY...

I'M SORRY!!

...DROPPED THE BOOK AT THE PERFECT MOMENT!!

That one's good too!

...

I GUESS EVERYBODY GETS LUCKY ONCE IN A WHILE.

AND SO YOU GUYS ARE GOING OUT ON A DATE?

NO WAY...

WHAT'S UP, TOUKA?

...

NOTH-ING.

UM...

...

WELL, I'M GOING THAT WAY, SO...

NO, THANK YOU. I HAD FUN!

THANK YOU SO MUCH FOR TODAY.

THAT YOU AND I ARE WALKING TOGETHER...

...ALL BECAUSE OF TAKATSUKI'S BOOK.

IT'S STRANGE THOUGH, ISN'T IT?

....?

...

IT'S KIND OF AMAZING...

To be continued in **Tokyo Ghoul**, Vol. 1

Ultraman

Story and Art by Eiichi Shimizu and Tomohiro Shimoguchi

Shinjiro is an ordinary teenager, but his father is the legendary Shin Hayata. When he learns that his father passed on the "Ultraman Factor" to him, and that he possesses incredible powers, nothing will ever be the same again.

RATED **T** FOR TEEN

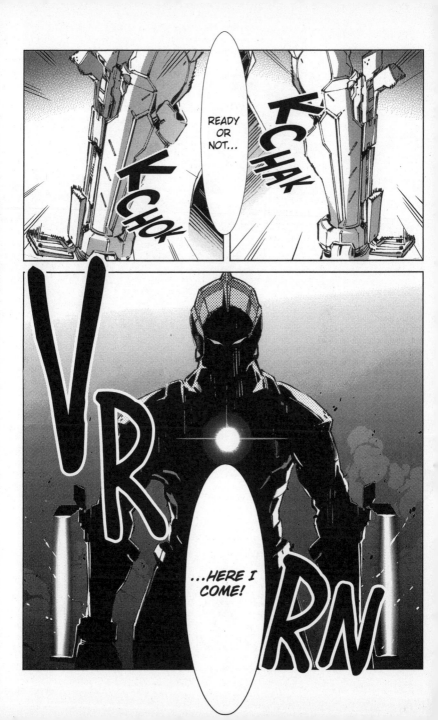

KRAK

To be continued in **Ultraman**, Vol. 1

My Hero Academia

Story and Art by Kohei Horikoshi

Middle school student Izuku Midoriya wants to be a hero more than anything, but he hasn't got an ounce of power in him. With no chance of ever getting into the prestigious U.A. High School for budding heroes, his life is looking more and more like a dead end. Then an encounter with All Might, the greatest hero of them all, gives him a chance to change his destiny...

A BODY...

... WITH A GOOD QUIRK.

HOPEFULLY THE PEOPLE DOWNSTAIRS WILL HELP US GET DOWN.

OF ALL THE ...!!

SCARY...

I'VE NO TIME, THOUGH! TRULY!!

GRR

WEEZ WEEZ

CRASH

...CAN I STILL BE A HERO?!

EVEN WITHOUT A QUIRK...

SHF

WAIT! UM...

NO!! I WILL NOT WAIT.

...MUST NEVER BE DAUNTED BY EVIL.

A SYMBOL OF PEACE WHO SAVES PEOPLE WITH A SMILE...

THAT LOWLIFE? HE COULD NEVER DO THIS TO ME!

WAS THAT WHEN YOU FOUGHT TOXIC CHAINSAW?

FIVE YEARS AGO ...?

You've done your homework.

CLENCH

THAT IS, I *ASKED* THAT IT NOT BE MADE PUBLIC.

THIS WAS NEVER MADE PUBLIC.

WITHOUT POWER, CAN ONE BECOME A HERO? NO, I SHOULD THINK NOT.

A PRO SHOULD ALWAYS BE READY TO RISK HIS LIFE.

...IS TO STAVE OFF THE OVERWHELMING PRESSURE AND FEAR I FEEL.

THE REASON I SMILE...

PA-
THETIC
...

DEALING
WITH THAT
FAN
LED
TO
THIS!!

I LOST
TRACK OF
TIME!

ZK
:THROB

SIGH

ハァ

h"
PLOD
h"
PLOD

P
A
T
H
E
T
I
C
!!

THIS
IS
REALITY
...

DON'T
CRY!
YOU
KNEW
ALREADY,
RIGHT?!

EVEN...THE
BEST
OF
THE BEST
SAID IT...

EVEN AS A
THIRD-YEAR,
HE STILL
CAN'T FACE
REALITY.

YOU NEED
TO BE
REALISTIC.

SNIFFLE
じわ...

IT'S
BECAUSE I
KNEW...THAT
I TRIED SO
DAMNED
HARD...

IT'S TIME
TO START
THINKING
SERIOUSLY
ABOUT YOUR
FUTURES!

To be continued in **My Hero Academia**, Vol. 1

The Demon Prince of Momochi House

Story and Art by Aya Shouoto

On her sixteenth birthday, orphan Himari Momochi inherits an ancestral estate that she's never seen. Momochi House exists in the barrier between the human and spiritual realms, and Himari is meant to act as guardian between the two worlds. But on the day she moves in, she finds three handsome squatters already living in the house, and one seems to have already taken over her role!

MOMOCHISANCHI NO AYAKASHI OUJI Volume 1 © Aya SHOUOTO 2013

THE DAY I TURNED 16, I RECEIVED A DOCUMENT STATING THAT...

PARDON MY INTRUSION... OH, I GUESS I SHOULD BE SAYING...

..."I'M HOME."

...I HAD INHERITED A MANSION KEPT IN TRUST.

Right?

KREE

...BUT THIS HOUSE IS THE ONE AND ONLY THING...

MY PARENTS MUST'VE BEEN BIG-TIME!

THIS IS INCREDIBLE...!

...SO I'VE NEVER HAD ANY FAMILY TIES.

MY PARENTS DIED IN AN ACCIDENT, AND I HAVE NO OTHER RELATIVES...

...LEFT TO ME BY MY REAL FAMILY.

TMP

TMP

THE ORPHANAGE WAS MY HOME FOR 16 YEARS. I LOVED EVERYONE THERE...

I'M GOING TO TAKE GOOD CARE OF IT!

...HIMARI.

IT'S VERY NICE TO HAVE YOU HERE...

WE'RE ALREADY ON A FIRST-NAME BASIS?!

I-IT'S NICE TO HAVE ME HERE...?

I'm not usually a sucker for gorgeous guys, but...

B L U S H

HMPH!

AND THAT'S ISE.

THIS IS YUKARI.

HELLO.

...WE'RE SQUATTERS.

I GUESS YOU COULD SAY...

!

...BUT IT'S TROUBLESOME FOR US IF YOU STAY.

THIS IS MY HOUSE! DIDN'T YOU SEE THE NAME BY THE ENTRANCE? IT'S MOMOCHI!

THAT MAY BE...

HOW ABSURD!

I'LL BE THE ONE MAKING THEM LEAVE!

I'M NOT GIVING UP.

JUST BECAUSE THEY'RE GORGEOUS DOESN'T MEAN THEY CAN DO WHATEVER THEY WANT.

My plan starts now!

KRRk

KRRk

CHIRP

CHIRP

I'LL MAKE THIS HOUSE SO GIRLY THEY'LL FEEL TOO UNCOMFORTABLE TO STAY.

HEE HEE HEE

BUT...

THERE ARE HOLES IN THE DOORS, AND THE ENTIRE HOUSE IS IN SHAMBLES.

WOOD-BURNING STOVE

BROOM

CLUTTER

CLUTTER

IT'S OBVIOUS BOYS LIVE HERE.

JUST LOOK AT THIS MESS.

NOT ONLY THAT...

THIS IS ROUGH!!

WHY ISN'T THERE A SINGLE ELECTRICAL APPLIANCE IN THIS HOUSE?!

Give me a vacuum cleaner...

EEK!

REEL

WHOOSH

-Okay.. what's next?

SHAMBLES

NOT BAD, IF I DO SAY SO MYSELF.

RHM

ARE YOU ALL RIGHT?

SUFF

YOU'RE NOT HURT, ARE YOU?

HUH?

AOI NANAMORI...

...

UM... SORRY I BROKE YOUR THING...

WHAT JUST HAPPENED?!

WHAT THE HELL DID YOU GIVE HIM?!

AOI, ARE YOU ALL RIGHT?

MY PHONE...

I HOPE IT COVERS EXPLOSIONS.

IT'S ALL RIGHT. LUCKILY I'VE GOT INSURANCE.

...

ARE YOU MAD?

WHY ARE YOU FOLLOWING ME AROUND?

HIMARI, I...

IT'S BEST IF YOU DON'T WANDER AROUND THE HOUSE TOO MUCH.

HIMARI...

WHAT? YOU WON'T CHANGE MY MIND, YOU KNOW.

Why are you wearing that thing?

OH...

I JUST SWEPT THAT AREA, AND YOUR ROBE IS DRAGGING DUST ALL OVER IT AGAIN.

IF YOU STAY HERE, SOMETHING BAD MIGHT HAPPEN.

I DON'T CARE! HE'S JUST TRYING TO SCARE ME INTO LEAVING.

SO WHAT?!

BUT...

...AND THEN HE PUTS HIS HANDS ALL OVER ME!

HE'S NICE AND TALKS IN THAT GENTLE VOICE OF HIS...

HIMARI...

CHILLS

IF YOU GET TOO CLOSE, YOU'LL BE CURSED BY THE OMAMORI-SAMA.

I WISH I HADN'T REMEM-BERED THAT.

NO, NO...

MOMOCHI HOUSE IS HAUNTED.

THIS HOUSE IS HUGE. I CLEANED ONLY A SMALL SECTION OF IT TODAY.

YOU'LL GET LOST.

We're sorry, Aoi!

COME ON, UNTIE US ALREADY.

APOLOGIZE TO HIMARI FIRST.

YOU SEEM LIKE...

Come on now.

...ONE BIG FAMILY.

To be continued in **The Demon Prince of Momochi House**, Vol. 1

Maid-Sama! 2-in-1 Edition

Story and Art by Hiro Fujiwara

As if being class president of a predominantly male high school isn't hard enough, Misaki Ayuzawa has a major secret—she works at a maid café after school! How is she supposed to keep her image of being ultra smart, strong and overachieving intact once school heartthrob Takumi Usui discovers her double life?!

Kaicho wa Maid Sama! © Hiro Fujiwara 2006/HAKUSENSHA, Inc.

HE WAS THE MAN I TRUSTED MOST, AND HE BETRAYED US.

MY FATHER DISAPPEARED ON US, LEAVING US ALONE WITH A HUGE DEBT.

AND I HAVE GOOD REASON.

I HATE GUYS.

SO NOW MY MOM AND I HAVE TO WORK EVERY SINGLE DAY. WE NEVER GET A BREAK.

THUD

UGH!

NOT MANY JOBS HAVE SUCH GREAT WORKING CONDI-TIONS.

BUT SINCE I JOINED THE STUDENT COUNCIL, I DON'T HAVE MUCH TIME.

I CAN'T LET ANYONE FROM SCHOOL SEE ME LIKE THIS...

WHOA—!

I KNEW I SHOULDN'T HAVE TAKEN THIS JOB.

TRASH

AND SINCE I'M PRESIDENT, I CAN'T LET MY GRADES SLIP. I COULDN'T HANDLE BOTH.

I DIDN'T HAVE ENOUGH STAMINA.

I'm not a genius or anything. I need energy to study.

Aren't you supposed to be really strong?

SO YOU HATE MEN BUT DECIDED TO WORK AT A MAID CAFÉ WAY OUT HERE.

WHY NOT DO MANUAL LABOR NEAR HOME?

THAT'S TOUGH...

HM.

...

...

...

WELL...

THAT SUCKS. SORRY TO HEAR IT.

YEAH.

...TUITION'S CHEAP?

SO YOU GO TO SEIKA DESPITE ALL THE GUYS 'CAUSE...

I CAN'T TELL WHAT HE'S THINK-ING...!

What's his game?

I WAS BRACED TO BE A LAUGHING-STOCK.

W-WHAT ARE YOU LOOKING AT?

HUH?

....!

...!

IS THAT ...

...USUI WATCHING US?

MOST GIRLS IN SCHOOL ARE CRAZY ABOUT HIM.

YOU LEAVE WHEN WE TALK ABOUT GUYS, SO MAYBE YOU DON'T KNOW?

Oh right.

UM, WHAT?

WAVE

Psh.

GUSH.

GUSH.

GUSH.

PLUS, JUST **LOOK** AT HIM! HE'S A RAY OF SUNSHINE WITH ALL THE JERKS HERE.

I HEAR HE STUDIED SHAOLIN KUNG FU UNTIL JUNIOR HIGH, AND HE'S SUPER STRONG!

THE GUYS ALL RESPECT HIM! HE ALWAYS GETS GOOD GRADES!

GUSH.

GUSH.

Sigh.

...

AHH, HE'S SO COOL! ♡

?

?

?

DRIP

DRIP

Right now, I don't understand girls at all.

HE'S THAT POPULAR?

Other schools all want him too.

NOT THAT THAT KEEPS GIRLS FROM ASKING HIM OUT.

BUT I GUESS HE'S **ALWAYS** BEEN SO POPULAR THAT NOW HE FINDS GIRLS BORING.

Hmph!

...THEN WHAT THE HECK IS HE DOING HERE NOW?!

B A M

GIRLS BORE HIM?

DOES THAT MEAN HE DOESN'T CARE ABOUT HOW HE SAW ME?

SIMMER SIMMER (Competitive Spirit)

Oh, there she is.

ISN'T HE EMBAR-RASSED TO BE HERE ALONE?! WHAT IS HE THINKING?

I DON'T GET IT!

BUT IF NOT...

YOU HAVE NO CLUE WHAT YOU'RE UP AGAINST!

WELL, HE'D BETTER BRACE HIMSELF! I NEVER BACK DOWN FROM A FIGHT!

IS HE HERE TO LAUGH AT ME?! TO SHOW HOW BRAVE HE IS?! OR... OR IS HE CHALLENGING ME?! ME=!

Ooooh! He's gorgeous!

SPARKLE
SPARKLE
SPARKLE
SPARKLE
SPARKLE
SPARKLE

WELCOME HOME, MASTER. ♡

WHO STAYS FOR AN HOUR AND ONLY ORDERS COFFEE?!

BACKYARD

SO HE ENJOYS TORMENTING ME!

PFFT!

▶▶ REPLAY

W...

Welcome home...

Piercing Stare

UGH, I FEEL SO SLUGGISH.

COUGH

I'VE GOT TOO MUCH ON MY MIND.

THIS IS HUMILIAT-ING.

!

HEY! CUT THAT OUT!

RUSTLE

And then—

Ha Ha!

I'M SO TIRED LATELY.

I'VE NEVER ...

...MET A GIRL LIKE THAT.

...

Let's see if he needs anything.

Lucky! ♥

He's here again.

DOESN'T HE REALIZE EVERY-ONE'S LOOKING AT HIM?

IS HE HAVING FUN WATCHING ME?

CHILL

HE'S HERE AGAIN.

...

HUH?

BLUSH

IS HE YOUR BOYFRIEND?

HE NEVER TAKES HIS EYES OFF YOU.

UH, NO ...

HEY, MISA-CHAN!

HE'S JUST MAKING FUN OF ME.

HE LOOKS WORRIED ABOUT YOU. IT'S SO SWEET. ♥

OKAY, SURE.

HUH? YOU WANT ME TO FILL OUT MY PROFILE?

SHHK

EXCUSE ME.

KOFF KOFF

STAFF LOUNGE

AS IF!

THERE'S NO WAY.

WORRIED?

NAME

MISAKI AYUZAWA

AGE (CLASS)

16 YRS. OLD (2-1)

BLOOD TYPE

B

HEIGHT

165 CM

WEIGHT

49 Kg

SPECIAL SKILL

AIKIDO

FAVORITE THING

WORKING HARD

...BUT IT'S STILL NOT AS HIGH AS BEFORE.

YOUR GRADE WENT WAY UP FROM LAST TIME...

ABOUT THE PRACTICE EXAM YOU TOOK THE OTHER DAY...

SURE.

OH, AYU-ZAWA. THANKS FOR COMING.

!

...TAKUMI USUI IN CLASS 2.

FLIP

HM?

HANG ON...

...INSTEAD OF FIRST.

YOU PLACED SECOND IN THE SCHOOL...

UM...

ARE YOU KIDDING ME?

WHO WAS NUMBER ONE?

I THINK IT WAS...

I THOUGHT I DID A LOT BETTER AFTER SWITCHING PART-TIME JOBS.

EVEN IF HE ACTUALLY IS WORRIED...

...THAT JUST MAKES IT...

UGH! I FEEL LIKE HE'S LOOKING DOWN ON ME.

HE'S PROBABLY LAUGHING AT ME FOR HAVING TOO MANY THINGS ON MY PLATE.

...EVEN MORE ANNOYING.

...THAT WE'RE READING A MAGAZINE.

THEY'RE UPSET...

Crud, it's the president.

OH, MISAKI.

WHAT'S UP?

monno

AIM TO BE

Man, you got guts!

Yeah, you tell her!

Yeah, but—

Nope, not cool.

No fair! You get to...

WHY CAN THE GIRLS READ THEM WHEN WE CAN'T?

BECAUSE YOU GUYS LEAVE INAPPROPRIATE ONES LYING AROUND!

YOU'RE TOO STRICT WITH US! YOU'VE GOTTA TREAT US ALL THE SAME.

INAPPROPRIATE HOW? YOU WON'T EVEN ALLOW COMICS CUZ SOME OF 'EM HAVE CENTERFOLDS!

MISAKI...

Yeah!

That's right!

HARD TO ARGUE WITH THAT.

...POLICE US, BE STRICT WITH THE GIRLS TOO!

IF YOU'RE GONNA

GRR... ...

THAT GOES FOR BOTH GUYS AND GIRLS.

PLEASE MAKE A LIST OF MAGA-ZINES YOU WANT TO READ.

WE'RE NOT GOING BACK TO HAVING STUFF LIKE THAT STREWN AROUND THE CLASSROOM.

BLATANTLY INAPPROPRIATE MATERIAL WILL BE BANNED!

ALL RIGHT, FINE!

I'LL REVIEW THE MAGAZINES ...

...AND MAKE A DECISION.

KOFF

IT'S FINE.

IT'S THE LEAST I CAN DO AS PRESIDENT.

I'm sure you'll agree that's fair— the council's mostly guys.

I'LL PERSONALLY GO THROUGH THEM AND DISCUSS IT WITH THE STUDENT COUNCIL. WE'LL DECIDE WHICH ONES TO ALLOW.

B-BUT THAT'S A **LOT** OF MAGAZINES! WE READ A **HUGE** VARIETY!

You seem over-worked already.

HER BEING CUTE DOESN'T MEAN YOU CAN TOUCH HER.

SMACK

!!

HUFF

SORRY...

...USUI.

DON'T NEED... YOUR HELP...

...

SORRY...

WOBBLE

ARE YOU OKAY?!

YOU'RE BURNING UP!

worse than I thought

...!

USUI?!

u...

SKREE

KOFF

IT'S OKAY.

JUST GET SOME REST.

WHEN I WOKE UP, I WAS IN MY ROOM.

THE CAFÉ HAD CALLED MY MOM, AND SHE PICKED ME UP.

THAT'S WHY I KEEP SAYING NOT TO PUSH YOURSELF SO HARD!

STAY IN BED AND SLEEP TODAY, OKAY?

OH! YOUR FRIEND FROM SCHOOL...

...LOANED YOU THAT SCARF SO YOU WOULDN'T BE COLD.

AFTER A DAY OF REST, MY HEAD CLEARED.

...OKAY.

TA-DA!

President

LOOK, PRESIDENT!

· · ·

THE WHOLE COUNCIL COLLECTED AS MANY MAGAZINES AS WE COULD.

We made an article list for each of them

We've gone through most of them and checked the content.

UM... ARE WE OVER-STEPPING?

YOU TRY TO DO EVERYTHING YOURSELF, SO WE NEVER KNOW WHAT TO DO.

Yeah, plus it was fun to read them all.

And then you made yourself sick!

· · ·

HUH?

THIS STUFF GETS DONE A LOT FASTER IF YOU LET US HELP.

THIS WAS A HUGE HELP.

THANKS!

I haven't really been doing my job...

YOU WOUND UP HAVING TO DO THE BOOKS, SO I THOUGHT I COULD AT LEAST HELP WITH THIS.

NO ...

NO ONE KNOWS ABOUT THE MAID THING?

HOW ABOUT...

...YOU BE MY OWN PERSONAL MAID FOR A DAY? ♡

WHAT?!

WAIT— I THOUGHT YOU WEREN'T INTERESTED IN GIRLS!

QUIET, YOU PERV!

WHY NOT? SEEMS FAIR TO ME.

WHAT THE HECK ARE YOU THINKING? ARE YOU AN IDIOT?

I'D BETTER FIND A NEW JOB. STAT.

THIS IS THE BEST.

...And he's having fun watching this situation unfold.

Meanwhile, these three have gotten hooked on seeing the president as a maid...

To be continued in **Maid Sama! 2-in-1 Edition**, Vol. 1